100磅的难题

【美】詹妮弗·达斯林◎著

【美】瑞贝卡·桑伯罗◎绘

范晓星◎译

天津出版传媒集团

新蕾出版社

图书在版编目 (CIP) 数据

100 磅的难题/(美)达斯林(Dussling,J.)著;
(美)桑伯罗(Thornburgh,R.)绘;范晓星译.—天津:
新蕾出版社,2015.8(2024.12 重印)
(数学帮帮忙·互动版)
书名原文:The 100-Pound Problem
ISBN 978-7-5307-6290-5

Ⅰ.①1… Ⅱ.①达…②桑…③范… Ⅲ.①数学–
儿童读物Ⅳ.①O1–49

中国版本图书馆 CIP 数据核字(2015)第 167705 号

出版发行: 天津出版传媒集团
　　　　　新蕾出版社
http://www.newbuds.com.cn
地　　址:天津市和平区西康路 35 号(300051)
出 版 人:马玉秀
电　　话:总编办 (022)23332422
　　　　　发行部 (022)23332679　23332351
传　　真:(022)23332422
经　　销:全国新华书店
印　　刷:天津新华印务有限公司
开　　本:787mm×1092mm　1/16
印　　张:3
版　　次:2015 年 8 月第 1 版　2024 年 12 月第 21 次印刷
定　　价:12.00 元

无处不在的数学

资深编辑　卢　江

　　人们常说"兴趣是最好的老师",有了兴趣,学习就会变得轻松愉快。数学对于孩子来说或许有些难,因为比起语文,数学显得枯燥、抽象,不容易理解,孩子往往不那么喜欢。可许多家长都知道,学数学对于孩子的成长和今后的生活有多么重要。不仅数学知识很有用,学习数学过程中获得的数学思想和方法更会影响孩子的一生,因为数学素养是构成人基本素质的一个重要因素。但是,怎样才能让孩子对数学产生兴趣呢?怎样才能激发他们兴致勃勃地去探索数学问题呢?我认为,让孩子读些有趣的书或许是不错的选择。读了这套"数学帮帮忙",我立刻产生了想把它们推荐给教师和家长朋友们的愿望,因为这真是一套会让孩子爱上数学的好书!

　　这套有趣的图书从美国引进,原出版者是美国资深教育专家。每本书讲述一个孩子们生活中的故事,由故事中出现的问题自然地引入一个数学知识,然后通过运用数学知识解决问题。比如,从帮助外婆整理散落的纽扣引出分类,从为小狗记录藏骨头的地点引出空间方位等等。故事素材全

部来源于孩子们的真实生活,不是童话,不是幻想,而是鲜活的生活实例。正是这些发生在孩子身边的故事,让孩子们懂得,数学无处不在并且非常有用;这些鲜活的实例也使得抽象的概念更易于理解,更容易激发孩子学习数学的兴趣,让他们逐渐爱上数学。这样的教育思想和方法与我国近年来提倡的数学教育理念是十分吻合的!

这是一套适合5~8岁孩子阅读的书,书中的有趣情节和生动的插画可以将抽象的数学问题直观化、形象化,为孩子的思维活动提供具体形象的支持。如果亲子共读的话,家长可以带领孩子推测情节的发展,探讨解决难题的办法,让孩子在愉悦的氛围中学到知识和方法。

值得教师和家长朋友们注意的是,在每本书的后面,出版者还加入了"互动课堂"及"互动练习",一方面通过一些精心设计的活动让孩子巩固新学到的数学知识,进一步体会知识的含义和实际应用;另一方面帮助家长指导孩子阅读,体会故事中数学之外的道理,逐步提升孩子的阅读理解能力。

我相信孩子读过这套书后一定会明白,原来,数学不是烦恼,不是包袱,数学真能帮大忙!

今天阳光明媚，又赶上放假，是个钓鱼的好日子。
正合沃特的心意。

人们都在海滩上钓鱼,但他们钓到的鱼却不多。沃特才不在乎,因为他要去对面的小岛钓鱼,这还要感谢罗杰表哥呢。

因为罗杰说可以借给沃特小船。罗杰可不是随便借人小船的,这条船是他爸爸亲手制造的,非常特别。

乘船须知
• 不要超载!
• 穿救生衣!
• 如果暴风雨来临,赶紧靠岸!

海滨安全委员会

5

沃特把东西放下。他的狗狗小补丁马上冲过来闻了闻装午餐的袋子。烤牛肉三明治！"不行，小补丁！"沃特对小狗说。小补丁显得很委屈。

　　沃特把小船翻过来，船尾写着几行字。

小船限重100磅。
罗杰

　　"哎呀，"沃特对小补丁说，"我觉得咱们的东西肯定超过 100 磅了。"

　　沃特知道自己的体重是 65 磅,学校体检时护士
告诉过他。他也知道小补丁的体重是 20 磅,兽医说
过的。他们两个加起来就有 85 磅了。

　　接下来，还有其他的东西：午餐哪，钓鱼竿哪，还有沉沉的背包。这些东西总共有多重呢？

"咱们没有秤,太糟糕了,是不是,小补丁?"沃特说。
他想到了一个主意。他可以自己做一个秤!

沃特从一艘旧船里找到一块木板。他把木板平放在岩石上，找到平衡点，这样看起来有点儿像跷跷板。

沃特的平衡秤

"好了，小补丁，"沃特说，"来给我帮个忙吧。"

沃特一指这个秤，小补丁就跳了上去。

"现在，我能知道我的东西跟你比的话，哪个更重。"沃特说。

沃特把背包放到秤上。秤纹丝不动。这说明背包没有小补丁重。

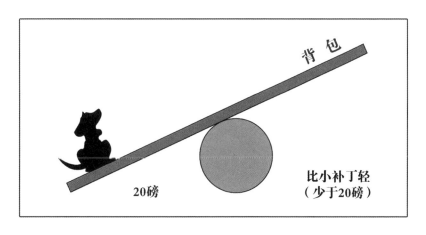

　　"现在，我来称称我的钓鱼竿和鱼饵盒。"沃特说。

　　秤还是一动不动。钓鱼竿和鱼饵盒也没有小补丁重。

　　"你知道吗？"沃特说，"我要把所有的东西都放到秤上！"

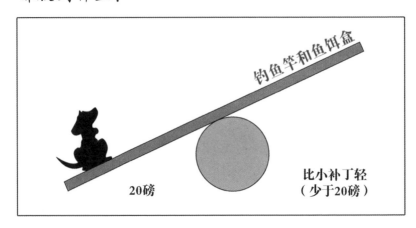

钓鱼竿和鱼饵盒

20磅

比小补丁轻
（少于20磅）

他刚一放上去，小补丁那边就弹了起来！

这下沃特知道了，这三样东西加起来比小补丁重。

午餐
钓鱼竿和鱼饵盒
背包

20磅

比小补丁重
（大于20磅）

如果我拿走一样东西呢？沃特琢磨着。

他告诉小补丁再坐到秤上，然后他把午餐拿了下来。

秤平衡了！

"太神了！"沃特说，"这说明钓鱼竿、鱼饵盒和背包加起来总共有20磅，和你一样重，小补丁！"

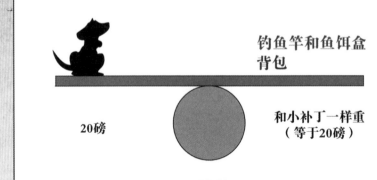

钓鱼竿和鱼饵盒
背包

20磅

和小补丁一样重
（等于20磅）

　　"午餐比背包轻多了，现在我知道该怎么办
了。"沃特说，"我每次只带几样东西过去，并且
留意船的载重量不超过 100 磅。"

第一趟，沃特带着午餐、钓鱼竿和鱼饵盒上了船。

他推小船的时候，小补丁一脸伤心地看着他。"对不起，宝贝。"沃特说，"要是我也带上你，咱们的船就超过 100 磅了。下次我再来接你吧！"

丹尼，生日快乐！

小船轻快地驶过港湾。这时,小船不远处的一只海鸟迅速地从水里叼起一条大鱼!

　　我希望我能和那只鸟一样幸运,沃特心想。

　　沃特把钓鱼工具和午餐运到小岛，然后又返回岸边，一共就用了几分钟的时间。小补丁还在等着。"上船吧，宝贝！"沃特说。

　　沃特看看他的背包。我还不太确定背包有多重，但是保险起见，我还是再划一趟吧，他想。

小补丁非常喜欢坐船。它一看到其他船，就"汪、汪"地问好。有条船上有只大狗，小补丁很兴奋，它又是叫，又是摇尾巴，直到那只大狗也朝它叫起来。

小船限重100磅。
罗杰

沃特来到小岛，小补丁一下蹿出了船，径直跑到午餐袋前，委屈地叫着。

　　"不可以，小补丁！"沃特说。一定是牛肉三明治太香了。小补丁最爱吃烤牛肉了。

哎呀，我得去取背包，可是我不能把小补丁和三明治单独留在一起。等我回来，三明治就该不见了，沃特心想。

"有了！"沃特说。答案很简单，他可以把小补丁留在小岛上，把午餐袋放在船上带在身边。"我很快就回来了！"他对小补丁说。

当沃特第三次划着船回到小岛，小补丁开始又跳又叫。"你这么高兴是因为见到我，还是因为三明治啊？"沃特跟小狗开玩笑地说。

他把船停到岸边，深深地吸了一口气。现在，他把所有想拿的东西都运到小岛上来了。

"小补丁，你猜怎么着？"沃特说，"我们该钓鱼啦！"小补丁跳进小船。

沃特把船划了出去,然后,将鱼线抛进了水里。终于,他开始钓鱼了,他来这儿就是为了钓鱼的!真是太惬意了!

　　突然，沃特的渔线动了一下，动静还不小呢。这说明鱼儿上钩了，而且是条大鱼！

钓鱼竿弯成了一张弓，可是沃特还是紧紧地握住不放。那条鱼挣来挣去，小补丁在一旁大叫着助威。

终于，沃特把渔线收了上来。

一条好大好重的鱼啊！哦，不！怎样才能让小船装下沃特、小补丁、钓鱼竿和鱼饵盒，还有这么大、这么沉的鱼呢？

沃特还没想好怎么办……

扑通!
小补丁已经想到了办法!

小补丁游上了岸，抖干身上的水。它为自己的聪明表现自我犒劳了一下，这一幕沃特在船上全部看到了。

沃特并不介意,毕竟他今天过得很开心。他钓到了一条大鱼,还解决了100磅的难题。但要是没有了小补丁的帮忙能行吗?当然不行喽!

重量

请看沃特的平衡秤。这个神秘的盒子和它们比起来哪个更重？

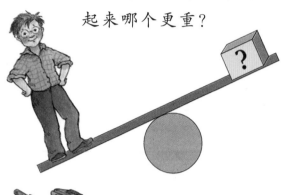

1.沃特更重。

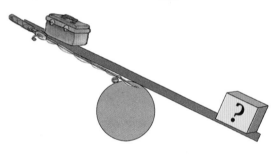

2.钓鱼竿和鱼饵盒更轻。

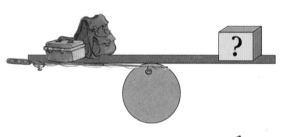

3.背包、钓鱼竿和鱼饵盒与神秘盒子一样重。

4.鱼和背包更重。

神秘的盒子里到底是什么？

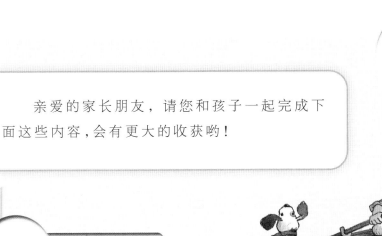

亲爱的家长朋友，请您和孩子一起完成下面这些内容，会有更大的收获哟！

提升阅读能力

• 阅读封面，和孩子聊聊，100磅的难题到底会是什么呢？

• 读过第6页之后，请孩子猜猜，沃特应该怎么做呢？读过第7页之后，请孩子比较一下自己和沃特的体重。在这个故事里，如果体重改变了的话，那沃特该怎样运东西才能到达小岛呢？

• 讨论故事的结尾。沃特是怎样到达小岛并钓到了大鱼？小补丁怎样实现了自己的心愿？

• 读过故事以后，请孩子想想，沃特总共在海滩和小岛之间来往了几次？

互动课堂

巩固数学概念

- 请孩子多看几遍沃特用自己做的秤来估算物品重量的部分。然后,请孩子想想,沃特能不能少划几次将东西运到小岛上呢?请孩子讲出自己的道理。

- 请看第 32 页的内容,巩固比较重量的概念。例如,请孩子用完整的句子来描述:小补丁比(沃特)轻很多。或者小补丁比(背包)重。

- 请把下面的词语写在小卡片上:秤、比什么重,比什么轻,一样重、平衡。解释这些概念在比较重量的时候如何应用。请孩子听写或者默写含有这些词语的句子,也可以让孩子给这些句子配上插图。

生活中的数学

- 自己做一个简单的平衡秤。帮孩子找一些物品来比较重量,并记录结果。然后,请孩子用相关词语来描述这些结果。

- 请孩子想想,在生活中,什么情况下需要知道物体的重量?例如,买蔬菜、水果的时候,寄东西的时候等等。

34

 不是最重的。

 比  重。

 比 轻。

 比 重。

这里有 4 个花瓶，它们分别重 3 磅、3.6 磅、4 磅、5.2 磅，你能把它们对号入座吗？

35

互动练习2

沃特的体重是 65 磅。

小狗小补丁的体重是 20 磅。

根据上面的信息，请判断下面的说法是否正确。对的打"√"，错的打"×"。

①10 磅的棉花比 10 磅的铁轻。（　　　）

②沃特的弟弟刚出生,体重约是 60 磅。（　　　）

③沃特的姐姐体重约是 70 磅。（　　　）

④1 头牛的体重约是 15 磅。（　　　）

⑤1 支铅笔约重 10 磅。（　　　）

⑥1 只小猫的体重约是 18 磅。（　　　）

在我们国家，常用的重量单位有：克、千克、吨。

1 千克 =1000 克

1 吨 =1000 千克

英国与美国通常使用磅作为重量单位，1 千克大约是 2 磅。

根据上述信息，请回答下面的问题。

①超市卖的盐每袋重 500 克，（　　　）袋盐重 1 千克？

②1 支牙膏重 100 克，（　　　）支牙膏重 1 千克？

1 枚 2 分硬币约重 1 克。

1 个苹果约重 200 克。

1 只山羊约重 35 千克。

根据上述信息，请在下面的空格中填上合适的单位。

①1 个排球重 450（　　　　）。

②上小学一年级的小明体重是 30（　　　　）。

③2 袋牛奶重 500（　　　　）。

④1 只小猫重 8（　　　　）。

⑤1 支铅笔重 10（　　　　）。

⑥1 个芒果重 280（　　　　）。

⑦1 只蓝鲸重 3（　　　　）。

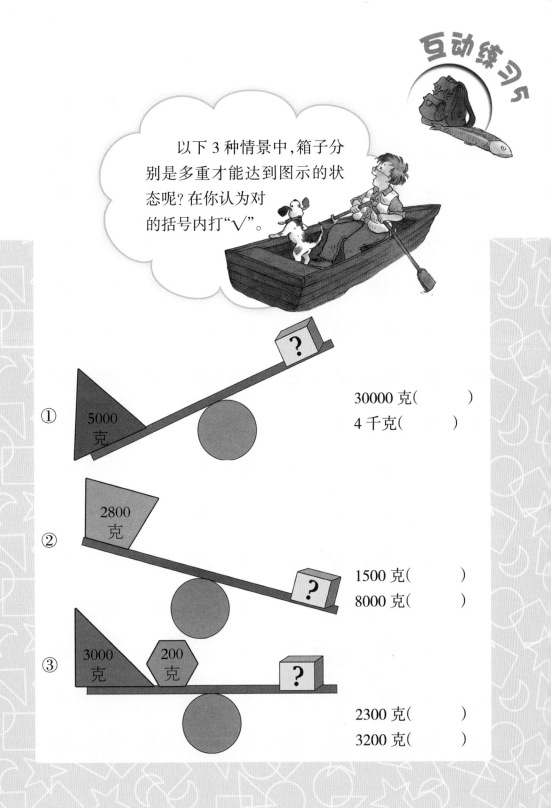

以下 3 种情景中,箱子分别是多重才能达到图示的状态呢? 在你认为对的括号内打"√"。

① 5000 克

30000 克(　　)
4 千克(　　)

② 2800 克

1500 克(　　)
8000 克(　　)

③ 3000 克　200 克

2300 克(　　)
3200 克(　　)

互动练习6

连一连

你觉得它们有多重？

400 千克

0.7 克

160 克

3 千克

妈妈买了 5 千克苹果,用去 15 元。小朋友,你知道 1 千克苹果多少元吗?

1 盒牛奶重 500 克,1 盒酸奶重 600 克,1 瓶水重 400 克。根据上述信息,回答下面的问题。

①牛奶和酸奶一共重多少克?

②水比酸奶轻多少克?

③台秤一次最多能称 1 千克的物品,哪两种物品可以同时称呢?

互动练习 1：

3 磅

3.6 磅

4 磅   5.2 磅

互动练习 2：
①×②×③√④×⑤×⑥√

互动练习 3：
①2　②10

互动练习 4：
①克②千克③克④千克⑤克
⑥克⑦吨

互动练习 5：
①4 千克②8000 克③3200 克

互动练习 6：

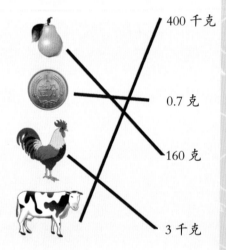

400 千克
0.7 克
160 克
3 千克

互动练习 7：
3 元
①1100 克
②200 克
③牛奶和水或酸奶和水

(习题设计：董惠平　骆　双)

THE 100-POUND PROBLEM

It was a bright sunny day. A no-school day.

A perfect day for fishing. And that's just what Walt was going to do.

People were fishing on shore. They hadn't caught much. But that didn't bother Walt. He was going to the island—thanks to his cousin Roger.

Roger said Walt could borrow his boat. He didn't let just anybody use it. His dad had made it, and it was special.

Walt put down his stuff. Right away his dog Patch started nosing the lunch bag. It was those roast beef sandwiches! "No, Patch!"Walt said. Patch looked guilty.

Walt turned the boat over. There was writing on it.

"Uh-oh,"Walt said to Patch."I bet we have more than 100 pounds!"

Walt knew he weighed about 65 pounds. The school nurse had told him so. He knew Patch weighed 20 pounds. That's what the vet had said. That was 85 pounds right there!

Then there was all his stuff. His lunch. His fishing gear. His heavy backpack. What did all that weigh?

"Too bad we don't have a scale, huh, Patch?" Walt said.

Then it came to him. He could make a scale!

Walt found a plank from an old boat. He balanced it over a rock. It looked a little like a seesaw.

"Okay, Patch," Walt said. "You're going to help me."

Walt pointed to his scale. Patch jumped on.

"Now I can find out what my stuff weighs compared to you," Walt explained.

Gently Walt put the backpack on the scale. The scale did not move. That meant the backpack weighed less than Patch.

"Now I'll weigh the fishing gear," said Walt.

The scale still did not move. So the gear was lighter than Patch, too.

"You know what?" Walt said. "I'm putting ALL my stuff on the scale!"

He did—and Patch's end swung up!

Now Walt knew that all three things together were heavier than Patch.

What if I take something away? Walt wondered.

He told Patch to sit on the scale again. Then Walt took his lunch off.

The scale balanced!

"Amazing!" Walt said. "That means the fishing gear plus the backpack weigh 20 pounds—the same as you, Patch!"

"The lunch bag is much lighter than the backpack. Now I know what to do." Walt said.

"I'll take just a few things at a time. And I'll be careful not to have more than 100 pounds in the boat."

For his first trip, Walt took his lunch and the fishing gear.

As he pushed off, Patch looked at Walt with sad eyes. "Sorry, boy," Walt said. "If I take you too, we'll be over 100 pounds. You can go next time."

The boat skimmed across the bay. Off to one side, a bird snapped a big fish right out of the water!

"I hope I'll be as lucky as that bird," Walt thought.

It took Walt only a few minutes to row his gear and his lunch to the island and back to shore. Patch was waiting. "Get in, boy!" Walt said.

Walt looked at his backpack. I'm not exactly sure how much the backpack weighs, he thought. I'll play it safe and make another trip.

Patch loved the boat ride. Every time he saw another boat, he barked hello. One boat had a big dog in it. Patch got very excited. He barked and wagged his tail until the other dog barked back.

When Walt reached the island, Patch jumped out of the boat and ran right to the lunch bag. He sniffed it and whined.

"No, Patch!" Walt cried. It was the roast beef sandwiches. Patch loved roast beef.

Uh-oh! I have to get my backpack. But I can't leave Patch alone here with my sandwiches. They'll be gone by the time I get back! Walt thought.

"I know!" Walt said. The answer was easy. He could leave Patch on the island—and take the lunch bag in the boat with him! "I'll be back in no time," he told Patch.

When Walt got back from his third trip, Patch started jumping and barking. "Are you glad to see me, or is it the sandwiches?" Walt joked.

He pulled ashore and took a deep breath. Now he had everything just where he wanted it.

"Guess what, Patch?" Walt said. "It's time to go fishing!" Patch jumped in the boat.

Walt rowed out and cast the line into the water. At last he was doing what he'd set out to do—he was fishing. It felt great.

All of a sudden there was a tug on Walt's line. A big tug! That meant a fish had the bait. A big fish!

The pole bent like a bow, but Walt held on tight. The fish fought and fought. Patch barked and barked.

Finally Walt reeled the fish in.

It was a big fish...a heavy fish! Oh, no! How could the boat hold Walt and Patch and the fishing gear and the big, heavy fish?

Before Walt could decide what to do...

SPLASH!

Patch had figured it out!

Patch swam to the island. He shook himself dry. And then, as Walt watched from the boat, Patch gave himself his own reward for being such a smart dog.

Walt didn't even mind. After all, he'd had a great day. He had caught a big fish, and he had solved the 100-pound problem. Could he have done it without Patch? No way!